Teaching Kids about Homophones and Homographs

(reproducible worksheets included)

flour

flower

Habakkuk Educational Materials

Published by Habakkuk Educational Materials

TEACHING KIDS ABOUT HOMOPHONES AND HOMOGRAPHS
(reproducible worksheets included)

ISBN (Paperback Edition): 978-1-954796-09-6

Printed and bound in the United States of America

Published by Habakkuk Educational Materials

Visit www.habakkuk.net

Table of Contents

Teaching Kids about Homophones and Homographs is a resource by Habakkuk Educational Materials meant to help students learn the difference between the words *homonyms*, *homophones*, *homographs*, and *heteronyms*. Through the use of colorful illustrations and sentences where the key words are used in context, children will learn to differentiate between homophones like *rain*, *reign*, and *rein* and *two*, *too*, and *to*. Reproducible worksheets are also available for individual practice and to assess student learning, and an answer key is available at the back of the book.

Kids will discover that homophone words are a type of homonym but that not all homonyms are spelled differently. For example, *ruler* is also a homonym, pronounced \rü-lər\, because it can refer to either a measuring tool or to a leader. In addition, they will learn that not all words that are spelled alike have the same meaning or pronunciation, as in the homographs (heteronyms) *dove*, referring to a bird, and *dove*, the past tense of *dive*. The definitions on the following page summarize the differences between the words *homonym*, *homophone*, *homograph*, and *heteronym*.

To contact Habakkuk Educational Materials or to download the free homophones matching game and bingo cards mentioned below, please visit the business website.

https://www.habakkuk.net/

FREE CENTER ACTIVITIES to complement this book are available by visiting the "Free Teaching Materials" page of the Habakkuk Educational Materials website at the address above. From the "Free Teaching Materials" page, click on the image of this book to view and download the homophones matching game, the homophones bingo cards (see the examples below), and more. (Note that these free materials also include homophones taught in *Homophones and Other Homonyms of Sight Words*, also by Habakkuk Educational Materials.)

son	sun

for	four

Homophone Words Bingo		
be	made	way
oar	son	flour
bare	caught	rough
knot	hear	accept

Homophone Words Bingo		
be	made	way
oar	son	flour
bare	caught	rough
knot	hear	accept

HOMONYM words sound alike, they may or may not be spelled alike, and they have different meanings, such as *hard* (not easy) and *hard* (not soft).

HOMOPHONE words sound alike, but they're spelled differently and have different meanings. (The word *phone* in *homophone* could help you to remember that homophone words sound alike.) Homophone words are a type of homonym that are not spelled alike (e.g., *four* and *for*).

HOMOGRAPH words are spelled alike, they may or may not sound alike, and they have different meanings. (The word *graph* in *homograph* could help you to remember that homograph words are spelled alike.)

HETERONYM words are spelled alike, but they sound differently and have different meanings. Heteronym words are a type of homograph that do not sound alike, such as \wĭnd\ and \wīnd\.

5

homophones

Directions: Point to the word on the left (which would be *accept* on the next page), read it, and have students repeat it. Then point to the word to the right of it (*except*) and let students read the word on their own. The teacher or parent reads (or explains) the definitions, which are italicized, and then the child reads the sentences where the key words are used in context. (Please also remember to go over the definition of homophones as discussed below.)

HOMO<u>PHONE</u> words sound alike, but they're spelled differently and have different meanings. (The word *phone* in *homophone* could help you to remember that homophone words sound alike.) Homophone words are a type of <u>homonym</u> that are not spelled alike (e.g., *four* and *for*).

Homophones

accept

Please **accept** these flowers!

*If you <u>accept</u> something,
you agree to take it.*

except

I put in every piece
except the blue one.

*<u>Except</u> means "other than." If you
replaced the word <u>except</u> in the
sentence above with <u>other than</u>,
it would still make sense.*

I will **accept** all these flowers **except** for the wilted one!

Underline the word that means that you are agreeing to receive.
Circle the word that means "other than."

Homophones

flour

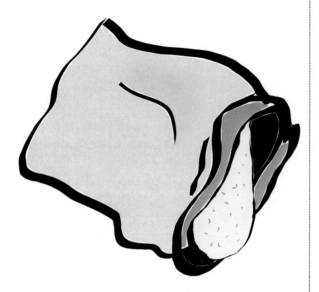

Flour is used to make bread.

*Flour is a powder
used for baked goods.*

flower

I picked a **flower** for you.

*A flower is a part of a
plant that smells good.*

Please don't spill **flour** on my pretty **flower**!

Underline the word that refers to a powder used for baked goods.
Circle the word that refers to a part of a plant that smells good.

four

Mike will be **four** on his next birthday.

Use <u>four</u> when you are talking about a number.

for

Thank you, Mom

I made this card **for** my mom.

Use <u>for</u> when you are NOT talking about a number.

My mom got **four** presents **for** Mother's Day.

Underline the word that refers to a number.
Circle the word that does NOT refer to a number.

meat | meet

© Good Studio / Adobe Stock

Roast is my favorite **meat** to eat. What is yours?

Meat is a food.

It's so nice to **meet** you!

Meet is coming to know a person or getting together with them.

Let's **meet** at the **meat** shop to buy some steak for dinner.

Underline the word that refers to a food.
Circle the word that refers to coming to know a person or getting together with them.

Homophones

 morning   mourning

Our rooster crows
every **morning**.

Morning is the early part of the day.

The kid has been **mourning**
ever since he lost his dog.

*Mourning means "to
feel or show sadness."*

The boy is **mourning** because he lost his dog this **morning**.

Underline the word that refers to the early part of the day.
Circle the word that means "to feel or show sadness."

soar

sore

Watch the eagle **soar** through the sky.

My arm is so **sore**!

To soar means "to fly or glide through the air."

Sore means "very painful."

My neck is **sore** from staring up to watch the eagle **soar**.

Underline the word that means "to fly or glide through the air."
Circle the word that means "very painful."

wear

I will **wear** the green shirt.

Wear means "to have on the body."

where

Where is it?

Where is a question word.

Where are you going
to **wear** that outfit?

Underline the word that means "to have on the body."
Circle the word that is a question word.

Homophones

weather | whether

What is the **weather** like outside today?

Weather refers to outdoor conditions, like heat, cold, rain, snow, and storms.

I need to decide **whether** to go.

Whether has to do with a choice between different possibilities.

We will go **whether** the **weather** is bad or not.

Underline the word that refers to outdoor conditions.
Circle the word that refers to a choice between different possibilities.

Homophones

buy

I went to the store to **buy** some food.

Buy means "to purchase something."

bye

Bye, everyone!

Bye means "goodbye."

by

Who was the book written **by**?

Use *by* for everything else.

Bye, everybody! I need to go **by** the store to **buy** some food.

Underline the word that means "to purchase something."
Circle the word that means "goodbye."
Highlight the word that does not mean "goodbye" or "to purchase something."

him hymn hem *

Listen to **him**.

We sung a **hymn** in church.

Grandma is fixing the **hem**.

Him can refer to a boy or man.

Hymn is a praise song.

The edge of fabric that has been folded over and sewn is the *hem*.

Grandma sang a **hymn** while she fixed the **hem** for **him**.

Underline the word that refers to a boy or man.
Circle the word that refers to a praise song.
Highlight the word that refers to the edge of fabric being folded over and sewn.

---

* Not everyone pronounces *hem* the same way they do *him* and *hymn*. It depends on where you are from. If you live in an area where *hem* is pronounced with the short *e* sound, you might skip over it or explain to students why it is included as a homophone of *him* and *hymn*.

Homophones

Mary | marry | merry

Mary is the mother of Jesus.

Mary is a girl or a woman's name.

The couple will **marry** in a church.

To marry is to become husband and wife.

Merry Christmas!

Merry means "happy."

Mary felt **merry** when Joseph asked her to **marry** him.

Underline the word that refers to a girl or to a woman's name.
Circle the word that means "to become husband and wife."
Highlight the word that means "happy."

Homophones

rain

My umbrella keeps me dry in the **rain**.

Water falling from the sky is <u>rain</u>.

reign

When did King Tut **reign** in Egypt?

To <u>reign</u> means "to rule."

rein

He used the **rein**s to guide his horse.

A <u>rein</u> is an object used to control the movement of a horse or similar animal.

A boy who would someday **reign**
as king held onto his **rein**s
while he rode home in the **rain**.

Underline the word that refers to water falling from the sky.
Circle the word that means "to rule."
Highlight the word that refers to an object used to control the movement of a horse.

Homophones

two

We have **two** dogs.

Two is a number.

too

It's too cold!

also

Use too to mean "also":
I want to go **too**.

Too is also used to indicate that something is more than desirable:
It's **too** cold to play outside.
I'm **too** sick to go to school.

to

Happy Birthday

TO you

"Happy birthday **to** you!"

Use to for everything else.

My brother is going **to** be **two** years old on his next birthday **too**.

Underline the word that refers to a number.
Circle the word that means "also."

more homonyms

Directions: Read the word in the singular form (without the colored -*s*) and let students repeat it in the plural form. (Please also remember to go over the definition of homonyms as discussed below.)

HOMONYM words sound alike, they may or may not be spelled alike, and they have different meanings, such as *hard* (not easy) and *hard* (not soft). The homonyms on the next few pages are spelled alike.

anchors

Let down the **anchor** so we can fish.

An <u>anchor</u> can hold a boat in place.

The **anchor** reported on the homeless crises.

An <u>anchor</u> can also be a person who reports the news on television.

caravans

It's fun to sleep in a **caravan** at the lake!

A <u>caravan</u> can be a trailer.

It was safer to travel in a **caravan** than alone through the dangerous desert.

A <u>caravan</u> can also be a group of merchants traveling together through the desert.

👂 courts ✍

The kids practiced on the **court**.

Sports like tennis and basketball are played on a court.

The **court** found them not guilty.

Justice is meant to be served in another kind of court.

👂 irons ✍

What do you think the man is making from **iron**?

Iron is a metal.

Please plug in the **iron**.

An iron is a tool used to remove wrinkles from clothes.

major**s**

My uncle is a **major**
in the military.

A major is a military officer.

She has a **major** in education.

*A major can also be a subject that
a college student specializes in.*

palm**s**

Palm trees grow in Florida
and other places.

A palm is a type of tree.

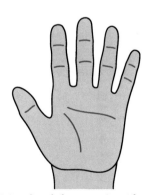

He holds us in the
palm of His hand.

A palm is also a part of the hand.

rulers

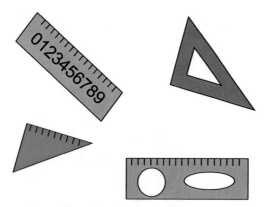

A **ruler** is 12 inches long.

A ruler is a measuring tool.

A king is a **ruler**.

A ruler can also be a leader.

tables

Please set the **table** for dinner.

A table is a piece of furniture used to eat on.

I need to record my weekly schedule on a **table**.

A table can also be a chart with columns and rows for organizing information.

Pronunciation Guide

ă (short *a*)	ā (long *a*)	ü	ar	ch
apple	ate	room	barn	chocolate
ĕ (short *e*)	ē (long *e*)	u	or	sh
epoch	we	book	corn	shop
ĭ (short *i*)	ī (long *i*)	ou	ər	th
iguana	hi	out, cow	teacher	thing
ŏ (short *o*)	ō (long *o*)	oi	ĕər	th
office	go	oil, boy	bear	this
ə (schwa)	ū (long *u*)	əl, əl	ĭər	zh
across	use	little, vowel	hear	measure

homographs (heteronyms)

Directions: Give both pronunciations of each word on a page and instruct students to repeat them. (Please also remember to go over the definition of homographs and heteronyms as discussed below.)

HOMO<u>GRAPH</u> words are spelled alike, they may or may not sound alike, and they have different meanings. (The word *graph* in *homograph* could help you to remember that homograph words are spelled alike.)

HETERONYM words are spelled alike, but they sound differently and have different meanings. Heteronym words are a type of <u>homograph</u> that do not sound alike, such as \wĭnd\ and \wīnd\. The words on the next few pages are heteronyms.

homographs (heteronyms)

bow
\bō\

The **bow** is gold.

The word <u>bow</u> can refer to a knot formed with two loops and two ends hanging down.

bow
\bou\

The frog took a **bow**.

The word <u>bow</u> means "to bend the body."

desert
\dĕz-ərt\

Have you ever visited a **desert**?

A <u>desert</u> is a dry and hot place.

desert
\dĭ-zərt\

Don't **desert** us!

Desert means "to abandon."

dove

\dəv\

The **dove** has a leaf in its beak.

A dove is a type of bird.

dove

\dōv\

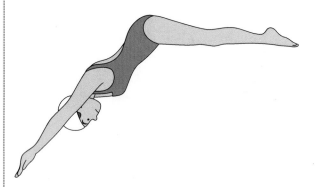

She **dove** into the water.

Dove is the past tense of dive.

excuse

\ĭk-skūs\

He made up an **excuse**
for not cleaning his room.

Excuse is a reason.

excuse

\ĭk-skūz\

Excuse me for coughing!

Excuse is an apology.

homographs (heteronyms)

lead

\lĕd\

The pencil **lead** is sharp.

Lead is the part of a pencil that can leave marks on a paper.

lead

\lēd\

Lead the camel home.

Lead means "to guide."

live

\lĭv\

I live in a house.

Live, pronounced as \lĭv\, means "to make a home of."

live

\līv\

The news is live.

Live, pronounced as \līv\, means it's happening now.

homographs (heteronyms)

object
\ŏb-jĭkt\

A toy is an **object**.

An <u>object</u> is an item.

object
\əb-jĕct\

I **object** to that question!

<u>Object</u> means "to disapprove of."

present
\prĕz-nt\

The **present** is wrapped.

A <u>present</u> is a gift.

present
\prə-zĕnt\

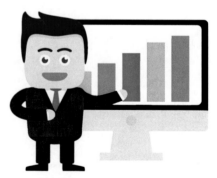

Let me **present**
this graph to you.

*If you <u>present</u> something,
you introduce it.*

homographs (heteronyms)

read
\rĕd\

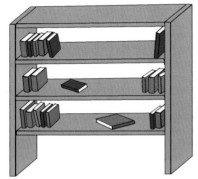

I already **read** these books.

Read, pronounced as \rĕd\, means it happened in the past.

read
\rēd\

I love to **read**!

Read, pronounced as \rēd\, can mean that it's happening in the present.

record
\rĕk-ərd\

My favorite song is on this **record**.

A record is an album where music is stored.

record
\rĭ-kord\

I **record** earthlings just for fun!

Record can mean "to videotape."

homographs (heteronyms)

SOW
\sō\

If a farmer is going to **sow** his seeds, he is going to plant them.

SOW
\sou\

The **sow** has a curly tail.

A sow is an adult, female pig.

tear
\tĕər\

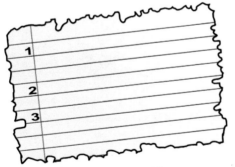

Why did you **tear** the paper?

Tear means "to rip."

tear
\tĭər\

A **tear** rolled down his face.

A tear is a water-like substance coming from the eye.

homographs (heteronyms)

wind
\wĭnd\

The **wind** is blowing me away!

Wind is a movement of air.

wind
\wīnd\

Wind me up!

To wind means "to twist around."

wound
\wünd\

I got more than one
wound in the accident.

A wound is an injury.

wound
\wound\

I need to be **wound** up.

Wound means it's twisted around.

homographs (heteronyms)

use
\ūs\

It's no **use**!

use
\ūz\

Use your umbrella to keep dry.

Reproducible worksheets for eBook readers: If you click on the link below, you will be directed to the Habakkuk Educational Materials website. Go to the "Free Teaching Materials" page of the website and click on the image of this book to view and download the worksheets shown on the following pages as well as the free center activities.

https://www.habakkuk.net/

Homonyms (Homophones)

Directions: Homophone words sound alike, but they're spelled differently and have different meanings. (The word *phone* in *homophone* could help you to remember that homophone words sound alike.) Homophone words are a type of <u>homonym</u> that are not spelled alike, such as *four* and *for*. Fill in each blank with a homophone word that makes sense in the context of the sentence.

accept: agree to receive **except:** other than	**flour:** a powder used for baked goods **flower:** a part of a plant
four: *Four* is referring to a number. **for:** *For* is not referring to a number.	**meat:** a food **meet:** to come to know a person or to get together with them

1. Please _____ this gift.   (accept, except)

   We ate all the pizza _____ for one slice.   (accept, except)

2. The recipe calls for _____.   (flour, flower)

   The _____ smells pretty.   (flour, flower)

3. This invitation is _____ you.   (four, for)

   I made _____ new friends at school today.   (four, for)

4. Please take the _____ out of the freezer.   (meat, meet)

   Did you _____ the new student?   (meat, meet)

HOMONYMS (HOMOPHONES)	
morning: the early part of the day **mourning:** to feel or show sadness	**soar:** to fly or glide through the air **sore:** very painful
wear: to have on the body **where:** a question word	
weather: outdoor conditions (e.g., heat, cold, rain, snow, storms) **whether:** a choice between different possibilities	
buy: to purchase something **bye:** goodbye **by:** Use *by* for everything else.	

5. Mom made pancakes for breakfast this _____.
   (morning, mourning)

   The girl has been _____ for her lost cat.
   (morning, mourning)

6. I feel _____ after practice.   (soar, sore)

   An eagle can _____ high.   (soar, sore)

7. _____ did you put your homework?   (wear, where)

   _____ something warm today.   (wear, where)

8. The _____ starts getting cooler in autumn.
   (weather, whether)

   I need to clean my room _____ I want to or not.
   (weather, whether)

9. We drove _____ your house.   (by, buy, bye)

   It's time to go. Tell your friend _____.   (by, buy, bye)

   He wants to _____ a new coat.   (by, buy, bye)

HOMONYMS (HOMOPHONES)	
him: a boy or man **hymn:** a praise song **hem:** the edge of fabric folded over and sewn	**Mary:** a girl or a woman's name **marry:** to become husband and wife **merry:** happy
rain: water falling from the sky **reign:** to rule **rein:** an object used to control the movement of a horse or similar animal	**two:** a number **too:** *also* or "more than desirable" **to:** Use *to* for everything else.

10. Give the book to _____.   (him, hymn, hem)

    Mom will sew the _____.   (him, hymn, hem)

    What is your favorite _____ to sing?   (him, hymn, hem)

11. I feel so _____!   (Mary, marry, merry)

    When did Joseph and Mary _____?
    (Mary, marry, merry)

    My sister's name is _____.   (Mary, marry, merry)

12. Kings and queens _____ in the United Kingdom.
    (rain, reign, rein)

    Take your umbrella in case of _____.   (rain, reign, rein)

    Don't let go of the horse's _____.   (rain, reign, rein)

13. May I play _____?   (two, too, to)

    I ate _____ pieces of pizza.   (two, too, to)

    Give the report cards _____ your parents.   (two, too, to)

    It's _____ hot to mow the lawn.   (two, too, to)

Homonyms

Directions: Some **homonym** words sound alike and are spelled alike, but they have different meanings, like *hard* (not easy) and *hard* (not soft). Circle the meaning of the underlined word.

1. Pull up the **anchor** so we can move to a different fishing spot.

   a tool to hold   a person who reports
   a boat in place   the news on TV

   My favorite news station has a new **anchor**.

   a tool to hold   a person who reports
   a boat in place   the news on TV

2. We are towing our **caravan** to the lake.

   a trailer   a group of merchants traveling
                      together through the desert

   Joseph's brothers saw a **caravan** of merchants coming.

   a trailer   a group of merchants traveling
                      together through the desert

3. The **court** found them guilty of all charges.

   a place where justice   an area where sports like tennis
   is meant to be served   and basketball are played

   The kids are shooting baskets on the **court**.

   a place where justice   an area where sports like tennis
   is meant to be served   and basketball are played

4. The pan is made of **iron**.

a metal   a tool used to remove wrinkles from clothes

Please **iron** the clothes.

a metal   a tool used to remove wrinkles from clothes

5. My cousin has a **major** in mathematics.

a military officer   a subject that a college student specializes in

Ask the Army **major** for permission.

a military officer   a subject that a college student specializes in

6. The **palm** has pretty leaves.

a type of tree   a part of the human hand

Hold it in the **palm** of your hand.

a type of tree   a part of the human hand

7. Use a **ruler** to measure the line.

a leader   a measuring tool

The president is a **ruler**.

a leader   a measuring tool

8. Mr. Green recorded his students' grades on a **table**.

a piece of furniture used to eat on   a chart with columns and rows to organize information

Please sit at the **table**.

a piece of furniture used to eat on   a chart with columns and rows to organize information

Homographs (Heteronyms)

Directions: Homograph words are spelled alike, they may or may not sound alike, and they have different meanings. (The word *graph* in *homograph* could help you to remember that homograph words are spelled alike.) **Heteronym words** are a type of homograph that do not sound alike, such as \wĭnd\ and \wīnd\. Circle the meaning of the underlined word.

1. Take a **bow** after your performance.

   to bend the body   to form a knot with two loops
                                        and two ends hanging down

   Tie the ribbon in a **bow**.

   to bend the body   to form a knot with two loops
                                        and two ends hanging down

2. I wouldn't want to live in the **desert**.

   to abandon   a dry and hot place

   Never **desert** a friend.

   to abandon   a dry and hot place

3. The **dove** is flying back.

   the past tense of *dive*   a type of bird

   He **dove** off the boat.

   the past tense of *dive*   a type of bird

40

4. **Excuse** me for bumping into you!

       an apology   a reason

He made up an **excuse** for not doing his homework.

       an apology   a reason

5. I broke my **lead**.

        to guide   the part of a pencil that can leave marks on a paper

Lead the cows back **home**.

        to guide   the part of a pencil that can leave marks on a paper

6. The football game is **live**.

    happening now, pronounced \līv\   to make a home of, pronounced \lĭv\

Some animals **live** in caves.

    happening now, pronounced \līv\   to make a home of, pronounced \lĭv\

7. I **object** to the way you are acting!

      to disapprove of   an item

An umbrella is an **object**.

      to disapprove of   an item

8. I have a report to **present**.

        a gift   to introduce

We need to get Grandma a birthday **present**.

        a gift   to introduce

Homographs (Heteronyms)

Directions: Homograph words are spelled alike, they may or may not sound alike, and they have different meanings. (The word *graph* in *homograph* could help you to remember that homograph words are spelled alike.) **Heteronym words** are a type of homograph that do not sound alike, such as \wĭnd\ and \wīnd\. Circle the meaning of the underlined word.

1. I **read** that book last week.

    past tense,   present tense,
    pronounced as \rĕd\   pronounced as \rēd\

   I like to **read** to my little brother.

    past tense,   present tense,
    pronounced as \rĕd\   pronounced as \rēd\

2. My mom is going to **record** the talent show.

    an album where   to videotape
    music is stored

   What songs are on that **record**?

    an album where   to videotape
    music is stored

3. The farmer is going to **sow** some seeds.

    an adult, female pig   to plant

   Then he is going to feed his **sow**.

    an adult, female pig   to plant

4. I got a **tear** in my jeans.

       rip   a water-like substance
                                         coming from the eye

I saw a **tear** in her eye.

       rip   a water-like substance
                                         coming from the eye

5. **Use** your key to open the door.

       pronounced as \ūs\   pronounced as \ūz\

It's no **use** to wash your car when it's raining.

       pronounced as \ūs\   pronounced as \ūz\

6. The **wind** is blowing my homework away!

       a movement of the air   to twist around

Wind up the yarn.

       a movement of the air   to twist around

7. I need a Band-Aid for my **wound**.

       an injury   twisted around

She **wound** up the yarn.

       an injury   twisted around

PAGE 7

Homophones

accept | except

Please **accept** these flowers!

If you _accept_ something, you agree to take it.

I put in every piece **except** the blue one.

Except means "other than." If you replaced the word _except_ in the sentence above with _other than_, it would still make sense.

I will **accept** all these flowers (**except**) for the wilted one!

Underline the word that means that you are agreeing to receive.
Circle the word that means "other than."

PAGE 8

Homophones

flour | flower

Flour is used to make bread.

Flour is a powder used for baked goods.

I picked a **flower** for you.

A _flower_ is a part of a plant that smells good.

Please don't spill **flour** on my pretty (**flower**)!

Underline the word that refers to a powder used for baked goods.
Circle the word that refers to a part of a plant that smells good.

PAGE 9

Homophones

four | for

Mike will be **four** on his next birthday.

Use _four_ when you are talking about a number.

Thank you, Mom

I made this card **for** my mom.

Use _for_ when you are NOT talking about a number.

My mom got **four** presents (**for**) Mother's Day.

Underline the word that refers to a number.
Circle the word that does NOT refer to a number.

PAGE 10

Homophones

meat | meet

Roast is my favorite **meat** to eat. What is yours?

Meat is a food.

It's so nice to **meet** you!

Meet is coming to know a person or getting together with them.

Let's (**meet**) at the **meat** shop to buy some steak for dinner.

Underline the word that refers to a food.
Circle the word that refers to coming to know a person or getting together with them.

PAGE 11

Homophones

morning | mourning

Our rooster crows every **morning**.

Morning is the early part of the day.

The kid has been **mourning** ever since he lost his dog.

Mourning means "to feel or show sadness."

The boy is (**mourning**) because he lost his dog this **morning**.

Underline the word that refers to the early part of the day.
Circle the word that means "to feel or show sadness."

PAGE 12

Homophones

soar | sore

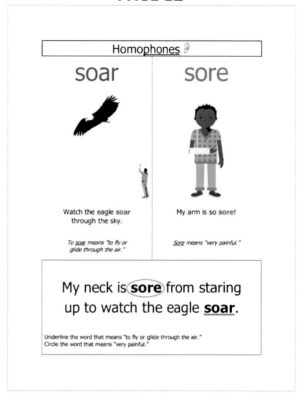

Watch the eagle **soar** through the sky.

To soar means "to fly or glide through the air."

My arm is so **sore**!

Sore means "very painful."

My neck is (**sore**) from staring up to watch the eagle **soar**.

Underline the word that means "to fly or glide through the air."
Circle the word that means "very painful."

PAGE 13

Homophones

wear | where

I will **wear** the green shirt.

Wear means "to have on the body."

Where is it?

Where is a question word.

(**Where**) are you going to **wear** that outfit?

Underline the word that means "to have on the body."
Circle the word that is a question word.

PAGE 14

Homophones

weather | whether

What is the **weather** like outside today?

Weather refers to outdoor conditions, like heat, cold, rain, snow, and storms.

I need to decide **whether** to go.

Whether has to do with a choice between different possibilities.

We will go (**whether**) the **weather** is bad or not.

Underline the word that refers to outdoor conditions.
Circle the word that refers to a choice between different possibilities.

PAGE 15

Homophones

buy | **bye** | **by**

I went to the store to **buy** some food. | **Bye**, everyone! | Who was the book written **by**?

Buy means "to purchase something." | *Bye means "goodbye."* | *Use by for everything else.*

Bye, everybody! I need to go **by** the store to **buy** some food.

Underline the word that means "to purchase something."
Circle the word that means "goodbye."
Highlight the word that does not mean "goodbye" or "to purchase something."

PAGE 16

Homophones

him | **hymn** | **hem** ·

Listen to **him**. | We sung a **hymn** in church. | Grandma is fixing the **hem**.

Him can refer to a boy or man. | *Hymn is a praise song.* | *The edge of fabric that has been folded over and sewn is the hem.*

Grandma sang a **hymn** while she fixed the **hem** for **him**.

Underline the word that refers to a boy or man.
Circle the word that refers to a praise song.
Highlight the word that refers to the edge of fabric being folded over and sewn.

* Not everyone pronounces *hem* the same way they do *him* and *hymn*. It depends on where you are from. If you live in an area where *hem* is pronounced with the short *e* sound, you might skip over it or explain to students why it is included as a homophone of *him* and *hymn*.

PAGE 17

Homophones

Mary | **marry** | **merry**

Mary is the mother of Jesus. | The couple will **marry** in a church. | **Merry** Christmas!

Mary is a girl or a woman's name. | *To marry is to become husband and wife.* | *Merry means "happy."*

Mary felt **merry** when Joseph asked her to **marry** him.

Underline the word that refers to a girl or to a woman's name.
Circle the word that means "to become husband and wife."
Highlight the word that means "happy."

PAGE 18

Homophones

rain | **reign** | **rein**

My umbrella keeps me dry in the **rain**. | When did King Tut **reign** in Egypt? | He used the **reins** to guide his horse.

Water falling from the sky is rain. | *To reign means "to rule."* | *A rein is an object used to control the movement of a horse or similar animal.*

A boy who would someday **reign** as king held onto his **reins** while he rode home in the **rain**.

Underline the word that refers to water falling from the sky.
Circle the word that means "to rule."
Highlight the word that refers to an object used to control the movement of a horse.

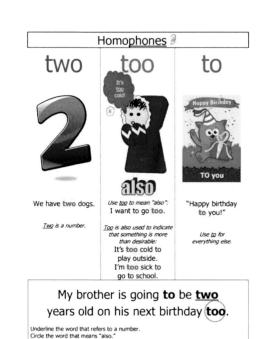

Homophones

two — We have **two** dogs. *Two* is a number.

too — It's too cold! — Use *too* to mean "also": I want to go **too**. — *Too* is also used to indicate that something is more than desirable: It's **too** cold to play outside. I'm **too** sick to go to school.

to — Happy Birthday — TO you — "Happy birthday **to** you!" — Use *to* for everything else.

My brother is going **to** be **two** years old on his next birthday (**too**).

Underline the word that refers to a number.
Circle the word that means "also."

Homonyms (Homophones)

Directions: Homophone words sound alike, but they're spelled differently and have different meanings. (The word *phone* in *homophone* could help you to remember that homophone words sound alike.) Homophone words are a type of <u>homonym</u> that are not spelled alike, such as *four* and *for*. Fill in each blank with a homophone word that makes sense in the context of the sentence.

accept: agree to receive	**flour:** a powder used for baked goods
except: other than	**flower:** a part of a plant
four: *Four* is referring to a number.	**meat:** a food
for: *For* is not referring to a number.	**meet:** to come to know a person or to get together with them

1. Please accept this gift.   (accept, except)

   We ate all the pizza except for one slice.   (accept, except)

2. The recipe calls for flour.   (flour, flower)

   The flower smells pretty.   (flour, flower)

3. This invitation is for you.   (four, for)

   I made four new friends at school today.   (four, for)

4. Please take the meat out of the freezer.   (meat, meet)

   Did you meet the new student?   (meat, meet)

HOMONYMS (HOMOPHONES)	
morning: the early part of the day	**soar:** to fly or glide through the air
mourning: to feel or show sadness	**sore:** very painful
wear: to have on the body	
where: a question word	
weather: outdoor conditions (e.g., heat, cold, rain, snow, storms)	
whether: a choice between different possibilities	
buy: to purchase something	
bye: goodbye	
by: Use *by* for everything else.	

5. Mom made pancakes for breakfast this morning.
   (morning, mourning)

   The girl has been mourning for her lost cat.
   (morning, mourning)

6. I feel sore after practice.   (soar, sore)

   An eagle can soar high.   (soar, sore)

7. Where did you put your homework?   (wear, where)

   Wear something warm today.   (wear, where)

8. The weather starts getting cooler in autumn.
   (weather, whether)

   I need to clean my room whether I want to or not.
   (weather, whether)

9. We drove by your house.   (by, buy, bye)

   It's time to go. Tell your friend bye.   (by, buy, bye)

   He wants to buy a new coat.   (by, buy, bye)

HOMONYMS (HOMOPHONES)	
him: a boy or man	**Mary:** a girl or a woman's name
hymn: a praise song	**marry:** to become husband and wife
hem: the edge of fabric folded over and sewn	**merry:** happy
rain: water falling from the sky	**two:** a number
reign: to rule	**too:** *also* or "more than desirable"
rein: an object used to control the movement of a horse or similar animal	**to:** Use *to* for everything else.

10. Give the book to him.   (him, hymn, hem)

    Mom will sew the hem.   (him, hymn, hem)

    What is your favorite hymn to sing?   (him, hymn, hem)

11. I feel so merry!   (Mary, marry, merry)

    When did Joseph and Mary marry?
    (Mary, marry, merry)

    My sister's name is Mary.   (Mary, marry, merry)

12. Kings and queens reign in the United Kingdom.
    (rain, reign, rein)

    Take your umbrella in case of rain.   (rain, reign, rein)

    Don't let go of the horse's rein.   (rain, reign, rein)

13. May I play too?   (two, too, to)

    I ate two pieces of pizza.   (two, too, to)

    Give the report cards to your parents.   (two, too, to)

    It's too hot to mow the lawn.   (two, too, to)

PAGE 38

Homonyms

Directions: Some **homonym** words sound alike and are spelled alike, but they have different meanings, like *hard* (not easy) and *hard* (not soft). Circle the meaning of the underlined word.

1. Pull up the **anchor** so we can move to a different fishing spot.
   - (a tool to hold a boat in place)
   - a person who reports the news on TV

   My favorite news station has a new **anchor**.
   - a tool to hold a boat in place
   - (a person who reports the news on TV)

2. We are towing are **caravan** to the lake.
   - (a trailer)
   - a group of merchants traveling together through the desert

   Joseph's brothers saw a **caravan** of merchants coming.
   - a trailer
   - (a group of merchants traveling together through the desert)

3. The **court** found them guilty of all charges.
   - (a place where justice is meant to be served)
   - an area where sports like tennis and basketball are played

   The kids are shooting baskets on the **court**.
   - a place where justice is meant to be served
   - (an area where sports like tennis and basketball are played)

PAGE 39

4. The pan is made of **iron**.
   - (a metal)
   - a tool used to remove wrinkles

   Please **iron** the clothes.
   - a metal
   - (a tool used to remove wrinkles)

5. My cousin has a **major** in mathematics.
   - a military officer
   - (a subject that a college student specializes in)

   Ask the Army **major** for permission.
   - (a military officer)
   - a subject that a college student specializes in

6. The **palm** has pretty leaves.
   - (a type of tree)
   - a part of the human hand

   Hold it in the **palm** of your hand.
   - a type of tree
   - (a part of the human hand)

7. Use a **ruler** to measure the line.
   - a leader
   - (a measuring tool)

   The president is a **ruler**.
   - (a leader)
   - a measuring tool

8. Mr. Green recorded his students' grades on a **table**.
   - a piece of furniture used to eat on
   - (a chart with columns and rows to organize information)

   Please sit at the **table**.
   - (a piece of furniture used to eat on)
   - a chart with columns and rows to organize information

PAGE 40

Homographs (Heteronyms)

Directions: **Homograph** words are spelled alike, they may or may not sound alike, and they have different meanings. (The word *graph* in *homograph* could help you to remember that homograph words are spelled alike.) **Heteronym** words are a type of homograph that do not sound alike, such as \wĭnd\ and \wīnd\. Circle the meaning of the underlined word.

1. Take a **bow** after your performance.
   - (to bend the body)
   - to form a knot with two loops and two ends hanging down

   Tie the ribbon in a **bow**.
   - to bend the body
   - (to form a knot with two loops and two ends hanging down)

2. I wouldn't want to live in the **desert**.
   - to abandon
   - (a dry and hot place)

   Never **desert** a friend.
   - (to abandon)
   - a dry and hot place

3. The **dove** is flying back.
   - the past tense of *dive*
   - (a type of bird)

   He **dove** off the boat.
   - (the past tense of *dive*)
   - a type of bird

PAGE 41

4. **Excuse** me for bumping into you!
   - (an apology)
   - a reason

   He made up an **excuse** for not doing his homework.
   - an apology
   - (a reason)

5. I broke my **lead**.
   - to guide
   - (the part of a pencil that can leave marks on a paper)

   Lead the cows back **home**.
   - (to guide)
   - the part of a pencil that can leave marks on a paper

6. The football game is **live**.
   - (happening now, pronounced \lĭv\)
   - to make a home of, pronounced \līv\

   Some animals **live** in caves.
   - happening now, pronounced \lĭv\
   - (to make a home of, pronounced \līv\)

7. I **object** to the way you are acting!
   - (to disapprove of)
   - an item

   An umbrella is an **object**.
   - to disapprove of
   - (an item)

8. I have a report to **present**.
   - a gift
   - (to introduce)

   We need to get Grandma a birthday **present**.
   - (a gift)
   - to introduce

Homographs (Heteronyms)

Directions: Homograph words are spelled alike, they may or may not sound alike, and they have different meanings. (The word *graph* in *homograph* could help you to remember that homograph words are spelled alike.) **Heteronym words** are a type of homograph that do not sound alike, such as \wind\ and \wind\. Circle the meaning of the underlined word.

1. I **read** that book last week.
   (past tense, pronounced as \rĕd\) — circled
   present tense, pronounced as \rēd\

   I like to **read** to my little brother.
   past tense, pronounced as \rĕd\
   (present tense, pronounced as \rēd\) — circled

2. My mom is going to **record** the talent show.
   an album where music is stored
   (to videotape) — circled

   What songs are on that **record**?
   (an album where music is stored) — circled
   to videotape

3. The farmer is going to **sow** some seeds.
   an adult, female pig
   (to plant) — circled

   Then he is going to feed his **sow**.
   (an adult, female pig) — circled
   to plant

4. I got a **tear** in my jeans.
   (rip) — circled
   a water-like substance coming from the eye

   I saw a **tear** in her eye.
   rip
   (a water-like substance coming from the eye) — circled

5. **Use** your key to open the door.
   pronounced as \ūs\
   (pronounced as \ūz\) — circled

   It's no **use** to wash your car when it's raining.
   (pronounced as \ūs\) — circled
   pronounced as \ūz\

6. The **wind** is blowing my homework away!
   (a movement of the air) — circled
   to twist around

   Wind up the yarn.
   a movement of the air
   (to twist around) — circled

7. I need a Band-Aid for my **wound**.
   (an injury) — circled
   twisted around

   She **wound** up the yarn.
   an injury
   (twisted around) — circled

Habakkuk Educational Materials would like to express gratitude to the websites https://openclipart.org/ and https://publicdomainvectors.org/ and their contributors for the illustrations used in this book.

You might also be interested in *Homophones and Other Homonyms of Sight Words*, a book filled with reproducible coloring sheets and worksheets, also by Habakkuk Educational Materials.